THIS WHERE'S WALDO? BOOK BELONGS TO:

HEY, WALDO FANS! FIVE INTREPID TRAVELERS ARE LOST IN EVERY SCENE! CAN YOU FIND THEM?

ODLAW   WIZARD WHITEBEARD   WENDA   WOOF   WALDO

AND IN EVERY SCENE, THE TRAVELERS HAVE EACH LOST SOMETHING PRECIOUS! CAN YOU FIND THESE ITEMS TOO?

WALDO'S KEY   WOOF'S BONE   WENDA'S CAMERA

WIZARD WHITEBEARD'S SCROLL   ODLAW'S BINOCULARS

For Waldo

First U.S. paperback edition 2007

Library of Congress Cataloging-in-Publication Data is available.

Library of Congress Catalog Card Number 97014990

ISBN 978-0-7636-4525-0 (hardcover)
ISBN 978-0-7636-3498-8 (paperback)

16 17 18 19 20 21 WKT 31 30

Printed in Shenzhen, Guangdong, China

This book was typeset in Optima and Wallyfont.

The illustrations were done in watercolor and water-based ink.

Candlewick Press
99 Dover Street
Somerville, Massachusetts 02144

visit us at www.candlewick.com

WHERE'S WALDO?

MARTIN HANDFORD

CANDLEWICK PRESS

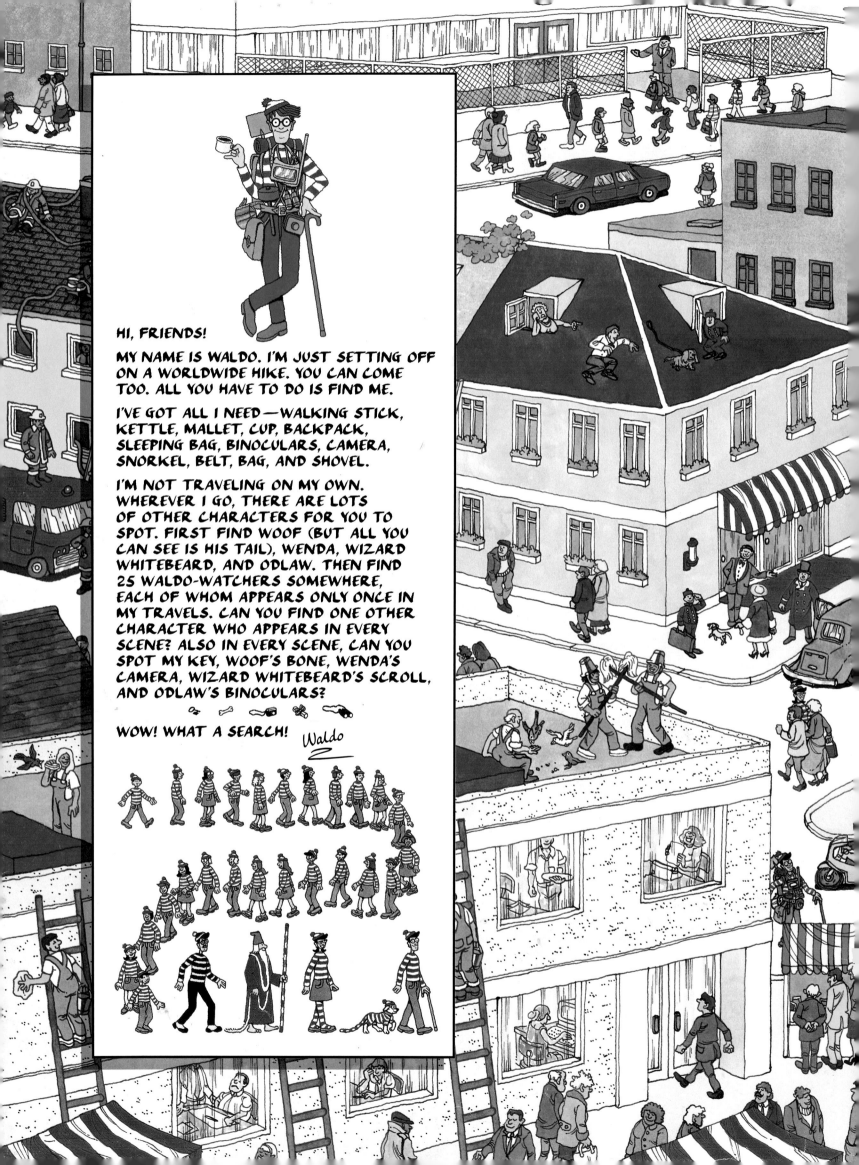

HI, FRIENDS!

MY NAME IS WALDO. I'M JUST SETTING OFF ON A WORLDWIDE HIKE. YOU CAN COME TOO. ALL YOU HAVE TO DO IS FIND ME.

I'VE GOT ALL I NEED—WALKING STICK, KETTLE, MALLET, CUP, BACKPACK, SLEEPING BAG, BINOCULARS, CAMERA, SNORKEL, BELT, BAG, AND SHOVEL.

I'M NOT TRAVELING ON MY OWN. WHEREVER I GO, THERE ARE LOTS OF OTHER CHARACTERS FOR YOU TO SPOT. FIRST FIND WOOF (BUT ALL YOU CAN SEE IS HIS TAIL), WENDA, WIZARD WHITEBEARD, AND ODLAW. THEN FIND 25 WALDO-WATCHERS SOMEWHERE, EACH OF WHOM APPEARS ONLY ONCE IN MY TRAVELS. CAN YOU FIND ONE OTHER CHARACTER WHO APPEARS IN EVERY SCENE? ALSO IN EVERY SCENE, CAN YOU SPOT MY KEY, WOOF'S BONE, WENDA'S CAMERA, WIZARD WHITEBEARD'S SCROLL, AND ODLAW'S BINOCULARS?

WOW! WHAT A SEARCH! *Waldo*

GREETINGS, WALDO-FOLLOWERS! WOW, THE BEACH WAS GREAT TODAY! ALL AROUND ME I SAW STRIPES ON TOWELS, CLOTHES, UMBRELLAS, AND BEACH HUTS. THERE WAS A SAND CASTLE WITH A REAL KNIGHT IN ARMOR INSIDE! FANTASTIC!

Waldo

WHERE'S WALDO? ON THE BEACH

TO: WALDO-FOLLOWERS HERE, THERE, EVERYWHERE

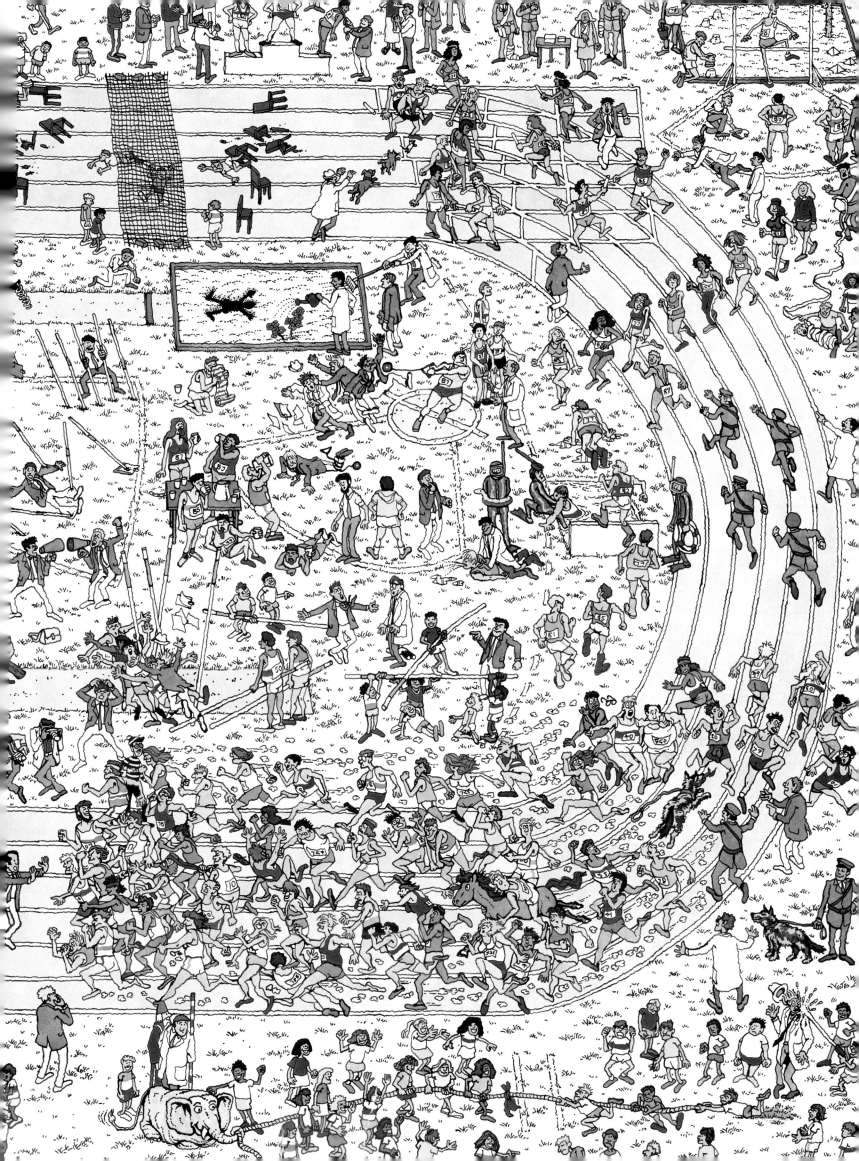

HEY, WALDO-WATCHERS!
I SAW SOME UNFORGETTABLE
SIGHTS TODAY: LOTS OF
RACKS AND TABLES FULL
OF COLORFUL THINGS; SOME
DEMONSTRATIONS GOING
WRONG; A MAN CHECKING
A WASHING MACHINE BY
WASHING HIS OWN CLOTHES IN
IT FIRST. PHEW! INCREDIBLE!

Waldo

WHERE'S DEPARTMENT STORE WALDO?

TO:
WALDO-WATCHERS
OVER THE MOON,
THE WILD WEST,
NOW

THE GREAT WHERE'S WALDO? CHECKLIST
Hundreds more things for Waldo-watchers to watch out for!

IN TOWN
A dog on a roof
A man on a fountain
A man about to trip over a dog's leash
A car crash
A happy barber
People on a sidewalk watching television
A puncture caused by an arrow
A tearful tune
A boy attacked by a plant
A sandwich
A waiter who isn't concentrating
Two firefighters waving at each other
A face on a wall
A man coming out of a manhole
A man feeding birds

SKI SLOPES
A man reading on a roof
A flying skier
A runaway skier
A backward skier
A portrait in snow
An illegal fisherman
Five people wearing striped scarves
Snow about to fall on two laughing men
Three skiers who have hit trees
An alpenhorn
Two broken flagpoles
A flag collector
Four people in yellow-hooded tops
A skier up a tree
A water-skier on snow
A yeti
Two skiing reindeer
A roof jumper
Someone crashing through five skiers

THE TRAIN STATION
Four shovels and five spades
A trolley carrying five suitcases
People being knocked over by a door
A man about to step on a ball
Three different times at the same time
A wheelbarrow baby carriage
A face on a train
Five people reading one newspaper
A show-off with a suitcase
Someone tripping over a dog
Two men with red-and-white-striped ties
A smoking train
A squeeze on a bench
A dog tearing a man's pants
A man sitting on a suitcase
Twenty cows
Someone desperately trying to lift a suitcase
Two suitcases spilling their contents
A broken weighing machine

ON THE BEACH
A dog and its owners wearing sunglasses
A man who is overdressed
A muscular man with a medal
A water-skier
A striped photographer
A punctured air mattress
A donkey who likes ice cream
A man being squashed
A punctured beach ball
A human pyramid
Three people reading newspapers
A cowboy
A human donkey
A radio
An irritated human stepping-stone
A red air mattress
Age and beauty
Two red-and-yellow umbrellas
Two men in tank tops, one without
A sand-castle show-off
Someone wearing suspenders
A cream-colored dog
Three protruding tongues
Two oddly fitting hats
Five sprinters
A towel with a hole in it
A punctured hovercraft
A boy who's not allowed any ice cream
Two caps with extra-long peaks

CAMPSITE
A bull in a hedge
Bullhorns
A shark in the canal
A bull seeing red
A careless kick
Tea in a lap
A low bridge
A person knocked over by a mallet
A man surprised undressing
A bicycle tire about to be punctured
Six dogs
An ineffective scarecrow
A teepee
Large biceps
Three campers with very long beards
A collapsed tent
A smoking barbecue
A fisherman catching old boots
An old-fashioned bicycle
A Boy Scout making fire
A roller hiker
A man blowing up a raft
Thirsty walkers
Runners on the road
A bull chasing two people
A campers' butler

AIRPORT
A flying saucer
A boy sitting with the revolving luggage
A leaking fuel pipe
Flight controllers playing badminton
A rocket
A tower on top of the control tower
Three watch smugglers
An airport worker resting on a plane
A forklift
A wind sock
Someone with a bucket and shovel
Six stewardesses in light-blue uniforms
A plane with giant tail wings
A fire engine and ten firefighters
Two passengers wearing white hats
A plane that doesn't fly
A flying ace
A pen and paper
Runners on a runway
Five men blowing up a balloon
Dracula
Three childish pilots
Eighteen airport workers with yellow caps

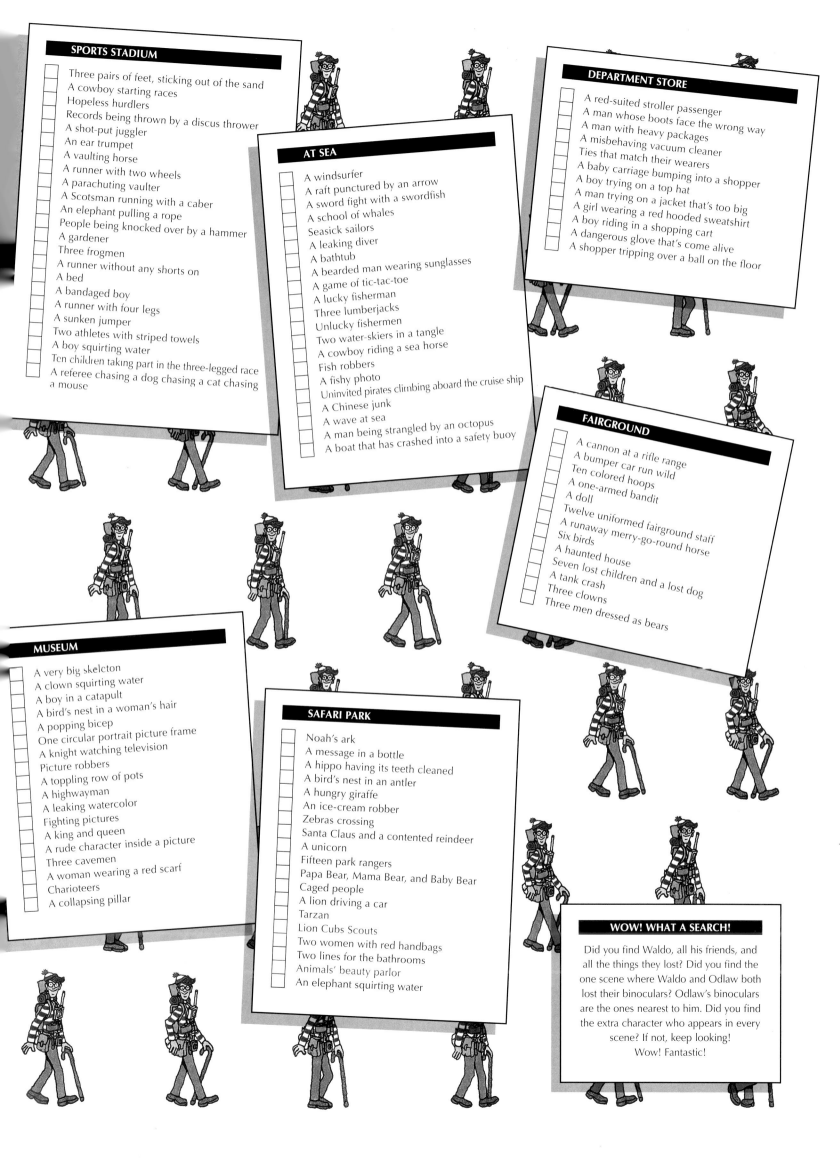

SPORTS STADIUM

- [ ] Three pairs of feet, sticking out of the sand
- [ ] A cowboy starting races
- [ ] Hopeless hurdlers
- [ ] Records being thrown by a discus thrower
- [ ] A shot-put juggler
- [ ] An ear trumpet
- [ ] A vaulting horse
- [ ] A runner with two wheels
- [ ] A parachuting vaulter
- [ ] A Scotsman running with a caber
- [ ] An elephant pulling a rope
- [ ] People being knocked over by a hammer
- [ ] A gardener
- [ ] Three frogmen
- [ ] A runner without any shorts on
- [ ] A bed
- [ ] A bandaged boy
- [ ] A runner with four legs
- [ ] A sunken jumper
- [ ] Two athletes with striped towels
- [ ] A boy squirting water
- [ ] Ten children taking part in the three-legged race
- [ ] A referee chasing a dog chasing a cat chasing a mouse

AT SEA

- [ ] A windsurfer
- [ ] A raft punctured by an arrow
- [ ] A sword fight with a swordfish
- [ ] A school of whales
- [ ] Seasick sailors
- [ ] A leaking diver
- [ ] A bathtub
- [ ] A bearded man wearing sunglasses
- [ ] A game of tic-tac-toe
- [ ] A lucky fisherman
- [ ] Three lumberjacks
- [ ] Unlucky fishermen
- [ ] Two water-skiers in a tangle
- [ ] A cowboy riding a sea horse
- [ ] Fish robbers
- [ ] A fishy photo
- [ ] Uninvited pirates climbing aboard the cruise ship
- [ ] A Chinese junk
- [ ] A wave at sea
- [ ] A man being strangled by an octopus
- [ ] A boat that has crashed into a safety buoy

DEPARTMENT STORE

- [ ] A red-suited stroller passenger
- [ ] A man whose boots face the wrong way
- [ ] A man with heavy packages
- [ ] A misbehaving vacuum cleaner
- [ ] Ties that match their wearers
- [ ] A baby carriage bumping into a shopper
- [ ] A boy trying on a top hat
- [ ] A man trying on a jacket that's too big
- [ ] A girl wearing a red hooded sweatshirt
- [ ] A boy riding in a shopping cart
- [ ] A dangerous glove that's come alive
- [ ] A shopper tripping over a ball on the floor

FAIRGROUND

- [ ] A cannon at a rifle range
- [ ] A bumper car run wild
- [ ] Ten colored hoops
- [ ] A one-armed bandit
- [ ] A doll
- [ ] Twelve uniformed fairground staff
- [ ] A runaway merry-go-round horse
- [ ] Six birds
- [ ] A haunted house
- [ ] Seven lost children and a lost dog
- [ ] A tank crash
- [ ] Three clowns
- [ ] Three men dressed as bears

MUSEUM

- [ ] A very big skeleton
- [ ] A clown squirting water
- [ ] A boy in a catapult
- [ ] A bird's nest in a woman's hair
- [ ] A popping bicep
- [ ] One circular portrait picture frame
- [ ] A knight watching television
- [ ] Picture robbers
- [ ] A toppling row of pots
- [ ] A highwayman
- [ ] A leaking watercolor
- [ ] Fighting pictures
- [ ] A king and queen
- [ ] A rude character inside a picture
- [ ] Three cavemen
- [ ] A woman wearing a red scarf
- [ ] Charioteers
- [ ] A collapsing pillar

SAFARI PARK

- [ ] Noah's ark
- [ ] A message in a bottle
- [ ] A hippo having its teeth cleaned
- [ ] A bird's nest in an antler
- [ ] A hungry giraffe
- [ ] An ice-cream robber
- [ ] Zebras crossing
- [ ] Santa Claus and a contented reindeer
- [ ] A unicorn
- [ ] Fifteen park rangers
- [ ] Papa Bear, Mama Bear, and Baby Bear
- [ ] Caged people
- [ ] A lion driving a car
- [ ] Tarzan
- [ ] Lion Cubs Scouts
- [ ] Two women with red handbags
- [ ] Two lines for the bathrooms
- [ ] Animals' beauty parlor
- [ ] An elephant squirting water

WOW! WHAT A SEARCH!

Did you find Waldo, all his friends, and all the things they lost? Did you find the one scene where Waldo and Odlaw both lost their binoculars? Odlaw's binoculars are the ones nearest to him. Did you find the extra character who appears in every scene? If not, keep looking!
Wow! Fantastic!